THE CHILDREN'S BIBLE

Volume 3

A Golden Press / Funk & Wagnalls, Inc. Book
Published by Western Publishing Company, Inc.

Classic™ binding
R. R. Donnelley & Sons Company
patents--U.S. pending
Distributed by Funk & Wagnalls, Inc. New York
Library of Congress Catalog Card Number: 81-81439
ISBN 0-8343-0040-0 (Volume 3)
ISBN 0-8343-0037-0 (12 Volume Set)

CONTENTS

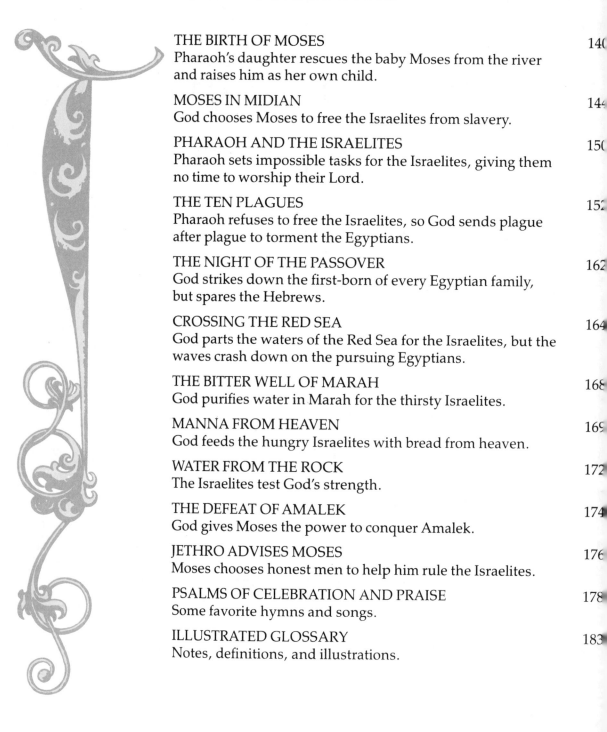

INTRODUCTION

The stories in this volume come from the Book of Exodus, the second book of the Bible. The word exodus means "departure." The first part of the Book of Exodus tells us about the departure of the Hebrew people from the land of Egypt. The Israelites had been enslaved in Egypt by the Egyptian rulers for many long years. The Book of Exodus describes first their hard life as slaves and then tells us about their flight to freedom.

The people of Israel first came to Egypt from Canaan because there was a terrible famine in their country. Jacob's sons and their families were saved by their exiled brother Joseph, who had become a ruler of Egypt. In times of drought or famine, it was common for people from other nations to travel to Egypt to seek food. This was because the Egyptians were skilled at watering their crops and storing food. They were also fortunate in having a steady supply of water from the Nile River.

At first the pharaoh had befriended the children of Israel and had given them good land. For years they lived peacefully and happily in Egypt. The pharaohs had been too busy with their wars against other kingdoms to notice the small group of Israelites who dwelled in their land. The Hebrews usually kept apart from the Egyptians and worked as farmers and shepherds, but some even worked in the Egyptian government.

Egypt soon became more powerful than it had ever been before. The nation of Egypt was rich in food and natural resources and the pharaohs had a great army of many thousands of men. The pharaohs had defeated all their enemies and now they governed their land in peace. They lived in great palaces with many wives and servants. But as the Hebrew people grew in numbers the Egyptians began to be frightened of them.

The Egyptians hated the Israelites because they had a different religion — the Israelites worshipped one God while the Egyptians worshipped many gods. The Egyptians could not understand why the Israelites sacrificed animals to their God. They did not understand that this was how the Israelites thanked their God for all the good things he provided for them.

The Egyptian fear and hatred of the Hebrew people grew worse over the years, even though the Israelites were peaceful and the Egyptians were powerful. There was no reason for the Egyptians to fear the Israelites, but nevertheless they were afraid that these strange people from Canaan would take over their country. Because of their fear and hatred, the Egyptian rulers enslaved the Israelite people.

The Israelites were put to work doing physical labor for the rich Egyptians. They had to make bricks for the pharaoh's palaces. The bricks were made from mud mixed with straw to give the bricks strength. The slaves had to carry the mud all the way from the banks of the Nile. The Israelites also carved large and heavy building stones out of limestone and sandstone. Some Israelites worked in copper mines. Egypt was rich in this metal and the Egyptians used it for many different purposes, such as making jewelry, pots, and cups.

The pharaohs liked to build great palaces made of many different kinds of stone. They created large and beautiful stone temples where the people of Egypt worshipped their gods. These temples had vast doorways and the roofs were held up by thick stone columns. At the time of Moses, the pharaohs were building palaces for themselves in the cities of Pithom and Rameses. The Israelites were the slave labor for these palaces and temples.

The Hebrew slaves were forced to work very hard. They worked all day long in the hot sun, and sometimes they fainted from the heat. They pulled great stones through the sand and up hills to where the pharaohs' palaces were being built. And the Hebrew slaves were always at the mercy of their cruel Egyptian masters.

Even while they were slaves, the Israelites never forgot their Lord. They sang about their God while they worked. They did this to keep themselves working. They sang about their great desire to be free. They sang about their own country because they never forgot God's promise to Abraham. And God heard the songs of his people. He did not forget his promise to make the land of Canaan their homeland. So he chose Moses to free them and lead them out of Egypt.

The Book of Exodus tells us about Moses' life. Moses was a Hebrew baby who had been condemned to death, but was saved by the pharaoh's daughter. She raised him as her own child, and Moses lived in the pharaoh's house when he was a young boy. He studied with the pharaoh's own children. He learned to read and write and learned how to play the many games and sports that the Egyptians enjoyed. Moses became a strong, intelligent young man. When he grew up, he was supposed to help the pharaoh govern Egypt.

Even though Moses grew up in the pharaoh's house, he never forgot that he was an Israelite. He helplessly witnessed the Egyptians' cruelty to the Hebrew slaves. But one day, when he saw an Egyptian beat an Israelite man, he became so angry that he killed the Egyptian. Then he had to flee into Midian to hide from the Egyptians because they would have killed him for committing murder.

Midian was a desert country. The Midianites were nomads, like the early Hebrews, who made their living by tending flocks of sheep and goats. While Moses was among the Midianites, he learned how to live in the desert. He learned to avoid the hot sun during the day and how to prepare himself for the cold desert nights. He was taught how to take care of the animals. Because he had grown up in the pharaoh's house Moses did not know how to do any of these things. He was to need all this new knowledge later in leading the Hebrew people across the desert towards Canaan.

The Book of Exodus recounts Moses' return to Egypt and the dramatic escape of the Hebrew slaves under his leadership. Many thousands of Israelites fled Egypt with Moses. They piled all the things they owned on their donkeys and set out into the desert with Egyptians pursuing them in chariots. The Israelites were afraid they would be captured and severely punished for their escape. But God protected the Israelites and they were not captured.

After their escape, life was still very difficult for the Israelites. Under Moses' leadership, they were trying to return to the land of Canaan, where their ancestors Abraham and Isaac had once lived. This was the land God had promised them as their home. During their many years as slaves, they had lived in the towns and countryside of Egypt. They no longer knew anything about traveling in the desert. They were often hungry and thirsty. Life in the desert was so hard that sometimes the children of Israel began to wonder whether they were not better off back in Egypt. Though they had been slaves in Egypt, at least they had always had food and water.

On their way back to Canaan, the Israelites spent many years in the desert traveling with their flocks of sheep and herds of cattle. They could not go by any of the main roads, because they were afraid of meeting patrols of the Egyptian army. The Israelites also had to make sure that they always stayed near water. It was difficult to carry enough water for so many people.

The Israelites met other groups of nomads in the desert. Sometimes these meetings were peaceful, and the nomads helped the Israelites with food and water and pointed out the way in the desert. But often the nomads feared each other and were afraid the strangers would take their precious food and water. They did not want to share the grazing land they had found for their flocks. Then the Israelites had to fight with the nomads. One such group of nomads was the Amalekites, who lived in the desert between Egypt and Canaan. When the Amalekites attacked the Israelites God helped the Israelites defeat them in battle, and they were able to continue their journey to Canaan.

During the flight from Egypt, God showed himself to be the special friend of the people of Israel. He showed the people how much he cared for them. He also taught them what they had to do to remain his chosen people. The Israelites could only survive in the desert because God gave them food and water. God never left his people alone in the desert during all their years of wandering, though they frequently angered him with their doubting, disobedience, and loss of faith.

Because they were his chosen people, God wanted the children of Israel to know his name. When God appeared to Moses in the burning bush, Moses asked God what his name was. God replied, "I am who I am." Jewish people call God "Adonai," which means Lord. God told Moses his name because he had chosen Moses, out of all the other Israelite men and women, as the person he wanted to lead his people to the Promised Land in Canaan.

In the stories of the Book of Exodus, God shows the world how strong he is. He punished even the mighty pharaohs because they would not free his people. He helped the Israelites defeat all their enemies in the desert. And these tales spread through the Bible lands, making other people fear the Hebrews and their powerful God.

The world heard how God chose the Hebrew slaves to be his people. God wanted his people to live again in their homeland in Canaan. He wanted them to worship him there and to show all the other nations how to worship him and serve him. In return for his protection, God asked the people to love him and to obey his commandments.

from the
BOOK OF EXODUS
Part 1

THE BIRTH OF MOSES

THE children of Israel were fruitful. They increased greatly in number and prospered, and the land of Egypt became filled with them.

But there arose a new king over Egypt who did not know Joseph and the great work he had done. This new Pharaoh said to his people:

"The children of Israel are more and mightier than we are. Let us deal wisely with them. For, if they continue growing in numbers, they may join our enemies and fight against us in time of war and go away from our land."

Therefore the Egyptians set taskmasters over the children of Israel and forced them to work for them. They built for Pharaoh the treasure cities of Pithom and Rameses. But the more the Egyptians oppressed them, the more the Israelites grew in strength and increased in number.

So the king of Egypt spoke to the Hebrew midwives, saying:

"When a Hebrew woman gives birth and you see that it is a son, then you shall kill him. But if it is a daughter she shall live."

But the midwives feared God and did not do as the king of Egypt commanded them. Instead, they let the men children live. So the king called the midwives and said to them:

"Why have you done this thing? Why have you let the men children live?"

"Because," answered the midwives, "the Hebrew women give birth without our knowing of it before we come to them."

God was pleased with the midwives and dealt well with them. And the people continued to increase and grow stronger. So Pharaoh commanded his people, saying:

"Every Israelite son that is born you shall cast into the river, and every daughter you shall let live."

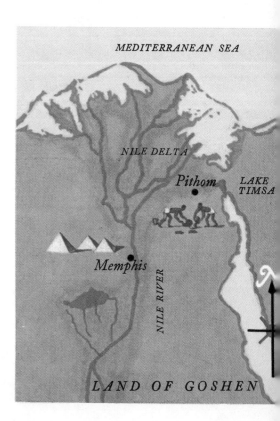

MEDITERRANEAN SEA

NILE DELTA

Pithom

LAKE TIMSA

Memphis

NILE RIVER

LAND OF GOSHEN

MOSES IN THE BULRUSHES

Now there was a man of the family of Levi whose wife bore him a son. And when she saw that he was a goodly child, she hid him for three months. Then, when she could no longer hide him, she took a basket made of bulrushes, daubed it with pitch and put the child into it. She took it and laid it in the reeds by the river's edge. And the baby's sister stood far away to watch what was done to him.

The daughter of Pharaoh came down to wash herself at the river, and her maids walked along by the river's side. When she saw the basket among the reeds, she sent her maids to fetch it.

When she opened the basket, she saw the child, and he was crying. So

she took pity on him and said, "This is one of the Hebrews' children."

The baby's sister came forward and said to Pharaoh's daughter:

"Shall I go and find a nurse from the Hebrew women to look after the child for you?"

"Go," said Pharaoh's daughter, and the girl went and called the child's mother. And Pharaoh's daughter said to the woman: "Take this child away and nurse it for me, and I will give you your wages."

So the mother took her child and nursed it. The child grew, and his mother brought him to Pharaoh's daughter, and he became her son. And she called him Moses (which means "drawn out") because, she said, "I drew him out of the water."

MOSES IN MIDIAN

ONE day, when Moses was grown up, he went out among his kinsmen and watched them labor. And he saw an Egyptian striking a Hebrew, one of his kinsmen. He looked this way and that way. When he saw that there was no one near, he killed the Egyptian and hid him in the sand.

When he went out the next day, he saw two Hebrew men fighting each other. He said to the one who was in the wrong:

"Why are you striking your own comrade?"

The man replied:

"Who made you a prince and judge over us? Do you intend to kill me as you killed the Egyptian?"

And Moses was afraid and said to himself, "What I have done must be known."

When Pharaoh heard of this, he tried to kill Moses, but Moses escaped from Pharaoh and went to live in the land of Midian.

There one day he sat down beside a well. Now the priest of Midian had seven daughters, and they came and drew water from the well, and filled the troughs to water their father's flock. Shepherds came and tried to drive them away, but Moses stood up and helped them, and watered their flock.

When they came home to their father, he said:

"How is it that you have come back so early today?"

And they answered:

"An Egyptian protected us from the shepherds, and also drew enough water for us, and watered the flock."

"Where is he?" their father asked. "Why have you left the man behind? Call him to eat with us."

Moses was happy to live with this man, and the man gave Moses his daughter Zipporah to be his wife.

Zipporah bore Moses a son, and he called him Gershom, which means "a stranger there," for he said, "I have been a stranger in a strange land."

And in due course it came to pass that the king of Egypt died. But the children of Israel were still oppressed and in slavery. In their suffering they cried out, and their cry carried up to God. He heard their groaning and remembered his promise to Abraham, to Isaac, and to Jacob.

And the Lord looked down upon the children of Israel and had pity on them.

GOD CALLS MOSES

At this time Moses was keeping the flock of his father-in-law, the priest of Midian, and he led the flock to the far side of the desert and came to the mountain of God, to Horeb. There the angel of the Lord appeared to him in a flame of fire out of the middle of a bush. Moses looked and saw that the bush burned with fire, but it was not destroyed.

And he said:

"I will stop here and see this great sight, and discover why the bush is not burnt."

When the Lord saw that he turned aside to see, he called out of the middle of the bush and said:

"Moses, Moses."

"Here am I," answered Moses.

"Do not come near," God said. "Take your shoes off your feet, for the place on which you are standing is holy ground."

And God said further:

"I am the God of your father, the God of Abraham, the God of Isaac, and the God of Jacob."

Moses hid his face, for he was afraid to look upon God.

And God said:

"I have seen the misery of my people who are in Egypt and I have heard their cries because of their taskmasters. I realize their sorrows. So

I have come down to deliver them out of the hand of the Egyptians, and to bring them out of that land into a land good and large, into a land flowing with milk and honey.

"Come now therefore, and I will send you to Pharaoh, so that you may lead forth my people, the children of Israel, out of Egypt."

But Moses said to the Lord:

"Who am I, that I should go to Pharaoh, and that I should lead forth the children of Israel out of Egypt?"

And God said:

"Certainly I will be with you, and this shall be a token that I have sent you: When you have brought forth the people out of Egypt, you shall worship God upon this mountain."

Then Moses said to the Lord:

"When I come to the children of Israel and say to them, 'The God of your fathers has sent me to you' and they say to me, 'What is his name?' what shall I say to them?"

And God said:

"This you shall say to the children of Israel: 'The Lord God of your fathers, the God of Abraham, the God of Isaac, and the God of Jacob has sent me to you.

" 'Yahweh is my name for ever, and by this I will be remembered to all generations.'

"Go and gather the elders of Israel together, and tell them all that I have said to you. They shall listen to your voice, and you and the elders of Israel shall go to the king of Egypt and say to him, 'The Lord God of the Hebrews has met with us, and we beg you to let us go three days' journey into the wilderness, so that we may worship the Lord our God.'

"And I am sure that the king of Egypt will not let you go, but I will stretch out my hand and strike Egypt with all my wonders. And after that he will let you go."

THE MIRACULOUS SIGNS

Then Moses said:

"But they will not believe me nor listen to my voice. They will say, 'The Lord has not appeared to you.'"

And God said to him:

"What is that in your hand?"

"A rod," answered Moses.

"Cast it on the ground," said God. So Moses cast it on the ground, and it became a serpent, and he shrank away from it. God ordered him, saying: "Put forth your hand and take it by the tail." So Moses put forth his hand and caught the serpent,

and it became a rod in his hand. And God said:

"Thus the people may believe that the Lord God of their fathers, the God of Abraham, the God of Isaac, and the God of Jacob has appeared to you."

And God said furthermore to Moses:

"Now put your hand against your breast."

He put his hand against his breast, and when he took it away, he saw that his hand was white as snow and diseased as though with leprosy. The Lord said:

"Put your hand against your breast again."

He put his hand against his breast once more. When he took it away, he saw that it had become again like his other flesh. And God said:

"It shall come to pass, if they will not believe you nor listen to you because of the first sign, that they will believe the second sign. But if they will not believe either of these two signs, nor listen to your voice, you shall take water from the river and pour it upon the dry land. And the water which you take out of the river shall become blood upon the dry land."

But still Moses said to the Lord:

"O my Lord, I am not a good speaker. I was not before, and I am not since you have spoken to me, your servant. I am slow of speech and have a slow tongue."

Then the Lord said to him:

"Who has made man's mouth? Who makes the dumb, the deaf, the seeing, or the blind? Is it not I, the Lord? So go now, and I will be with your mouth, and I will teach you what you shall say."

But Moses said, "O my Lord, send, I beg you, someone else."

And God became angry with Moses, and he said:

"Is not Aaron the Levite your brother? I know that he can speak well.

Also I see that he is coming out to meet you, and when he sees you he will be glad in his heart. You shall speak to him and put words in his mouth. And I will be with your mouth and with his, and will teach you both what you shall do.

"He shall be your spokesman to the people. He shall take the place of a mouth for you, and you shall take the place of God for him. And you shall take this rod in your hand, to do signs with it."

MOSES RETURNS TO EGYPT

Moses went and returned to his father-in-law and said to him:

"Let me go, I beg you, and let me return to my kinsmen who are in Egypt, and see whether they are still alive."

"Go in peace," said he to Moses.

And God said to Moses in Midian:

"Go, return to Egypt, for all the men are dead who sought your life."

So Moses took his wife and his sons, and set them upon an ass, and he returned to the land of Egypt, taking the rod of God in his hand. And the Lord said to Moses: "When you return there, see that you do before Pharaoh all the wonders which I have put in your hand. But I will harden his heart so that he shall not let the people go."

And the Lord said to Aaron:

"Go into the wilderness to meet Moses."

Aaron went and met Moses at the mountain of God, and kissed him. And Moses told Aaron all that the Lord had said to him, and all the signs that he had told him to do.

Moses and Aaron went and gathered together all the elders of the children of Israel, and Aaron spoke all the words which the Lord had spoken to Moses, and did all the signs for the people to see.

The people believed. And when they heard that the Lord had visited the children of Israel, and that he had seen their suffering, they bowed their heads and worshiped.

PHARAOH AND THE ISRAELITES

OSES and Aaron went before Pharaoh and spoke to him, saying: "These are the words of the God of Israel: 'Let my people go, so that they may hold a feast to me in the wilderness.'"

But Pharaoh said:

"Who is the Lord, that I should obey his voice and let Israel go? I do not know the Lord, nor will I let Israel go. Why do you, Moses and Aaron, interfere with the work of the people? Get back to your tasks. The people of the land are many now, and you make them rest from their labors."

The same day Pharaoh gave orders to the taskmasters of the people and their officers, saying:

"You shall no longer give the people straw to make bricks, as you have done in the past. Let them go and gather straw for themselves. But the number of bricks which they made before, you are still to demand of them. You shall require as much from them as before, for they are idle. That is why they cry out saying, 'Let us go and sacrifice to our God.' Let the men be given more work, so that they may have no time to listen to empty talk."

The taskmasters and officers went out and spoke to the people, saying:

"Pharaoh says, 'I will not give you straw. Go out and get straw where you can find it, for you shall make no fewer bricks than before.'"

So the people were scattered throughout all the land of Egypt. And their taskmasters kept after them, saying, "Fulfill your works and your daily tasks, as when there was straw." And the officers of the children of Israel, whom Pharaoh's taskmasters had set over them, were beaten and asked, "Why have you not fulfilled your task of making bricks both yesterday and today, as many as you have made before?"

So the officers of the children of Israel came and cried out to Pharaoh, saying:

"Why do you deal with your servants in this way? No straw is given to us, and we are told, 'Make bricks.' We are beaten, but the fault is with your own people."

"You are idle," Pharaoh answered. "That is why you say, 'Let us go and sacrifice to the Lord.'

"So go now and work. There shall be no straw given to you. And still you shall have to make as many bricks as before."

The officers of the children of Israel, seeing that the number of bricks to be made was to be no less, went forth from Pharaoh. On their way, they met Moses and Aaron, and they said to them:

"May the Lord look upon you and judge you, because you have made us hateful in the eyes of Pharaoh and in the eyes of his servants, so that they want to kill us."

GOD SPEAKS TO MOSES

Then Moses returned to the Lord and said: "Lord, why have you treated these people so badly? Why have you sent me? For since I came to Pharaoh to speak in your name, he has done evil to these people, and you have done nothing to save them."

Then God said to Moses:

"Now you shall see what I will do to Pharaoh. For with a strong hand he shall let the people go. With a strong hand he will drive them out of his land.

"For I am the Lord. I appeared to Abraham, to Isaac, and to Jacob by the name of God Almighty. I made a promise to them, to give them the land of Canaan.

"Say to the children of Israel, 'I am the Lord, and I will free you from the burdens of the Egyptians, and I will take you out of slavery. I will make you my people, and I will be to you a God. I will bring you to the land I promised to give to Abraham, to Isaac, and to Jacob. And I will give it to you and your descendants.' "

Moses told the children of Israel all that the Lord had said. But they did not listen to Moses in their suffering and their misery. And God said to Moses:

"You shall say all that I have to tell you. And Aaron your brother shall speak to Pharaoh, telling him to send the children of Israel out of his land. But I will harden Pharaoh's heart and perform many signs and miracles in the land of Egypt. Still Pharaoh will not listen to you, so I will lay my hand on Egypt and bring forth my armies and my people out of Egypt by my great judgments.

"The Egyptians shall know that I am the Lord when I stretch forth my hand upon Egypt and bring the children of Israel out from among them."

THE
TEN PLAGUES

OSES and Aaron did as the Lord commanded them. Moses was eighty years old and Aaron was eighty-three years old when they spoke to Pharaoh.

And God spoke to Moses and to Aaron, saying:

"When Pharaoh asks you to show him a miracle, then you shall say to Aaron, 'Take your rod and cast it before Pharaoh,' and it shall become a serpent."

So Moses and Aaron went before Pharaoh and they did as the Lord had told them. Aaron cast down the rod before Pharaoh and his servants, and it became a serpent.

Then Pharaoh called all the wise men and the sorcerers and the magicians of Egypt. In the same manner each man threw down his rod, and they all became serpents. But Aaron's rod swallowed up their rods.

THE PLAGUE UPON THE RIVER

Then the Lord hardened Pharaoh's heart, so that he did not listen to them, as the Lord had said. And God spoke to Moses, saying:

"Pharaoh's heart is hardened. He refuses to let the people go. So go to Pharaoh again in the morning. He is going out to the river. You shall stand by the river until he comes, and take

in your hand the rod which was turned into a serpent.

"You shall say to him, 'The Lord God of the Hebrews has sent me to you, saying, "Let my people go, so that they may worship me in the wilderness." Yet up to this time you would not listen. Now these are the words of the Lord: "In this way you shall know that I am the Lord." Behold, I will strike the rod that is in my hand upon the water in the river, and it shall be turned to blood. And the fish in the river shall die, and the river shall smell foul, and the Egyptians

shall not want to drink of the river.' "

Then God said further to Moses: "Say to Aaron, 'Take your rod, and stretch out your hand upon the waters of Egypt, upon her streams, upon her rivers, upon her ponds and all her pools of water, so that they may become blood, so that there may be blood throughout all the land of Egypt, in all the pails of wood and jugs of stone.' "

Moses and Aaron did everything as the Lord commanded. Aaron lifted up his rod and struck the water in the river, in the sight of Pharaoh and his servants, and all the water in the river turned to blood. And the fish in the river died, and the river smelled foul, so that the Egyptians could not drink the water of the river.

But the magicians of Egypt could do the same with their enchantments, so Pharaoh's heart was hardened. And he did not listen to Moses and Aaron, as the Lord had said.

Pharaoh turned and went into his house, his heart unmoved by this, and all the Egyptians dug round about the river for water to drink, for they could not drink of the water of the river.

THE PLAGUE OF FROGS

Seven days passed after the Lord had struck the waters. Then God said to Moses:

"Go to Pharaoh, and say to him, 'These are the words of the Lord: "Let my people go, so that they may worship me. If you refuse to let them go, then I will send a plague of frogs over all your country. The river shall bring forth quantities of frogs, which shall come up into your house, and into your bedroom and on to your bed, and into the houses of your servants and upon your people, and into your ovens and into your cooking bowls. And the frogs shall swarm over you and your people and over all your servants."'"

And God commanded Moses, saying:

"Tell Aaron to stretch out his hand with your rod over the streams, over the rivers and over the ponds, and cause the frogs to come upon the land of Egypt."

Aaron stretched out his hand over the waters of Egypt, and the frogs came up and covered the land.

But the magicians did the same with their enchantments, and they brought up frogs upon the land of Egypt.

Then Pharaoh called for Moses and Aaron, and said:

"Pray to the Lord, and ask him to take the frogs away from me and from my people. And I will let the people go, in order that they may make sacrifices to the Lord:

Moses said to Pharaoh:

"When shall I pray for you, and for your servants and for your people, to have the frogs destroyed among you and your houses, so that they may remain only in the river?"

"Tomorrow," Pharaoh said. Then Moses said:

"It shall be as you ask, so that you may know that there is no one like the Lord our God. The frogs shall be taken from you and from your houses, and from your servants and from your people. They shall remain only in the river."

Moses and Aaron left Pharaoh, and Moses prayed to the Lord about the frogs which he had brought down upon Pharaoh. The Lord did according to the prayer of Moses. The frogs died out of the houses, out of the villages, and out of the fields. And they were gathered up in heaps, and the whole land smelled of them.

THE PLAGUE OF LICE

But when Pharaoh saw that they were gone, he hardened his heart and would not listen to Moses and Aaron, just as the Lord had said. So God said to Moses:

"Tell Aaron to stretch out his hand with his rod and strike the dust of the land, so that it may become lice throughout all the land of Egypt."

Moses did so. Aaron stretched out his hand with his rod and struck the dust of the earth. And it became lice on the men and on the beasts throughout all Egypt.

The magicians tried to do the same with their enchantments, but they could not. So they said to Pharaoh:

"This is the work of God."

THE PLAGUE OF FLIES

But Pharaoh's heart was hardened and he would not listen to them, as the Lord had said.

So God spoke to Moses, saying:

"Rise up early in the morning, and stand before Pharaoh as he comes down to the river, and say to him,

"Go, sacrifice to your God here in Egypt."

But Moses said:

"We cannot worship our God before the eyes of the Egyptians because our sacrifices would seem vile to them. Our worship is an abomination to the Egyptians and if we made sacrifices to the Lord, would they not stone us?

'These are the words of the Lord: "If you will not let my people go, so that they may worship me, I will send swarms of flies upon you, upon your servants and upon your people, and into your houses. The houses of the Egyptians and all their land shall be full of swarms of flies. But on that day I will separate from this land the land of Goshen, in which my people dwell, so that no swarms of flies shall be there. From tomorrow I will put a division between my people and your people, so that you may know that I am the Lord over all the earth." ' "

And the Lord did so. There came a great swarm of flies into the house of Pharaoh, into his servants' houses and into all the land of Egypt. The land was ruined by the swarm of flies; they descended upon everything.

Pharaoh called for Moses and Aaron, and said to them:

We will go three days' journey into the wilderness and sacrifice to our God according to his command."

And Pharaoh said:

"I will let you go and sacrifice to the Lord your God in the wilderness. Only you shall not go very far away. Speak to your God for me."

"When I leave you," Moses answered, "I will pray to the Lord that the swarms of flies may leave Pharaoh, his servants and his people tomorrow. But Pharaoh must not deal dishonestly any more in not letting the people go to sacrifice to the Lord."

Moses left Pharaoh and prayed to the Lord, and the Lord did as Moses asked. He removed the swarms of flies from Pharaoh, from his servants and from his people. There remained not one.

But again Pharaoh hardened his heart and would not let the people go.

THE PLAGUE UPON THE CATTLE

Then God said to Moses:

"Go to Pharaoh and tell him that the Lord says, 'Let my people go, so that they may serve me. If you refuse, the hand of the Lord shall be upon your cattle, upon the horses, the asses, the camels, the oxen and the sheep. There shall be a terrible plague. But the Lord shall separate the cattle of Israel from the cattle of Egypt, and nothing shall die that belongs to the children of Israel.'"

And the Lord appointed a set time, saying, "Tomorrow I shall do this thing." And on the following day, all the cattle of Egypt died. But not one of the cattle of the children of Israel died.

Pharaoh sent his messengers to see, yet still his heart was hardened, and he did not let the people go.

THE PLAGUE OF SORES

So God said to Moses and to Aaron:

"Take handfuls of ashes from the furnace, and let Moses sprinkle them in the air in the sight of Pharaoh. They shall become fine dust throughout the land of Egypt, and they shall become sores upon man and upon beast throughout the land."

They took ashes from the furnace and stood before Pharaoh. And Moses sprinkled them in the air, and they caused sores to break out upon man and upon beast.

The magicians could not stand before Moses because of the sores, for they were on the magicians and on all the Egyptians.

But still Pharaoh's heart was hardened and he would not listen to them, as the Lord had said.

158

THE PLAGUE OF HAIL AND FIRE

And God said to Moses:

"Rise up early in the morning and stand before Pharaoh and say to him, 'These are the words of the Lord God of the Hebrews: "I will send all my plagues on you, your servants and your people. You will know that there is none like me in all the earth. You still will not let my people go, so tomorrow about this time I will cause it to rain a terrible hail as has not been seen in Egypt since its foundation. Therefore gather your cattle now, and all that you have in your fields, for the hail shall come down upon every man and beast found in the fields and not brought home, and they shall die." ' "

Those of Pharaoh's people who feared the word of the Lord brought their servants and cattle to the houses, but those who did not believe the word of the Lord left their servants and their cattle in the field.

And in accordance with the Lord's command, Moses stretched out his rod towards the heavens, and the Lord sent thunder and hail. And fire ran upon the ground. Fire mixed with hail and nothing like it had been seen in the land since Egypt became a nation. The hail struck everything in the fields, man, beast and plant, and broke down every tree in the fields. Only in the land of Goshen, where the children of Israel were, was there no hail.

Pharaoh sent for Moses and Aaron, and said to them:

"I have sinned this time. The Lord is just and I and my people are wicked. Pray to the Lord that there may be no more thunder and hail, and I will let you go. You shall stay no longer."

Moses went from Pharaoh, out of the city, and spread his hands to the Lord, and the thunder and hail were stopped. But when Pharaoh saw this, he sinned even more and hardened his heart, and he would not let the children of Israel go.

THE PLAGUE OF LOCUSTS

God said to Moses:

"I have allowed all these things to take place so that you may tell your son, and your son's son, what things I have done in Egypt, and the signs that I have given so that you may know that I am the Lord."

Moses and Aaron came again before Pharaoh, and said to him:

"This is what the Lord God of the Hebrews says:

'How long will you refuse to humble yourself before me? If you will not let my people go, tomorrow I will bring locusts into your country. They shall cover the face of the earth so that it cannot be seen. They shall eat everything that has been left after the hail and every tree growing in the fields. They shall fill your house and the houses of all your servants, and the houses of all the Egyptians. Your fathers and your fathers' fathers have seen nothing like it in all their lives.' "

And they turned around and went out from Pharaoh.

And Pharaoh's servants said to him:

"How long shall this man bring suffering to us? Let the men go and worship their God. Do you not see that Egypt is destroyed?"

Moses and Aaron were brought again to Pharaoh, and he said to them:

"Go and worship the Lord your God. But who shall go with you?"

Moses answered: "We will go with our young and our old people, with our sons and with our daughters, with our flocks and our herds, for we must hold a feast to the Lord."

"Let the Lord be with you," said Pharaoh, "if I ever let you and your little ones go. But this shall not be, for you have an evil plan. Let only the men go and worship the Lord." And they were driven out from Pharaoh's presence.

Then Moses did as the Lord had commanded, and stretched out his rod over the land of Egypt.

And the Lord caused an east wind to blow over the land all that day and all that night. And when it was morning the east wind brought the locusts. The locusts went over all the land of Egypt. Never before or afterwards had anyone seen so many locusts. The whole land was darkened with them, and they ate every plant and all the fruit from the trees that the hail had left. Not one green thing re-mained throughout all the land o Egypt.

Pharaoh called quickly for Mose and Aaron and said:

"I have sinned against the Lor your God and against you. Forgiv me, I beg of you, this once, and pra to the Lord your God that this plagu may be taken from me."

Moses left Pharaoh and entreate the Lord.

The Lord then sent a very stron; west wind, which took away the locust and blew them into the Red Sea. No one locust was left in the whole lanc of Egypt.

But still Pharaoh's heart was hard ened and he would not let the childre: of Israel go.

HE PLAGUE OF DARKNESS

So God said to Moses:

"Stretch out your hand towards the
eavens, so that there may be darkness
ver the land of Egypt, a darkness so
hick that it may be felt."

Moses stretched forth his hand to-
ards the heavens, and there
as a thick darkness through-

out the land of Egypt for three days.
The Egyptians could not see one another, and no one moved from his
place for three days. But all the children of Israel had light where they lived.

Pharaoh called Moses and said:

"Go, worship the Lord. Only leave
your flocks and herds behind. Your
children may go with you."

"You must allow us sacrifices that
we may offer to the Lord our God,"
Moses answered. "Our cattle must go
with us. Not one animal shall be left
behind, for we do not know how we
must worship the Lord until we reach
the place appointed."

But again Pharaoh's heart was hardened, and he would not let them go.
And the Lord said to Moses:

"Yet one plague more will I bring
upon Pharaoh and upon Egypt. Afterwards he will let you go. Indeed he
will drive you out altogether."

THE PLAGUE UPON THE
FIRST-BORN

Moses came again before Pharaoh
to tell him the words of the Lord:
" 'About midnight I will go out into
Egypt, and all the first-born in the land
of Egypt shall die, from the first-born
child of Pharaoh upon his throne, to
the first-born of the maidservant at the
mill, and all the first-born of cattle.
And there shall be a great cry throughout all the land of Egypt, such as was
never heard before and shall never
be again.

"But none of the children of Israel
shall suffer in any way, neither they nor
their animals. Thus you shall see how
the Lord has put a difference between
the Egyptians and Israel.' "

And Moses went out from Pharaoh
in a great anger, but Pharaoh's heart
was still hardened, and he would not
let the children of Israel go.

THE NIGHT OF THE PASSOVER

MOSES called for all the elders of Israel and spoke to them, in accordance with the command of the Lord, saying:

"Take a lamb from your flocks, according to the size of your families, and kill it. Take a bunch of herbs and dip it in the blood that is in the basin, and strike with the blood the top and the two side posts of the doorways of your houses. And none of you shall go out of his house until morning.

"You shall roast the lamb and shall eat the meat with unleavened bread and with bitter herbs. When you eat it you shall be ready to depart, with your shoes on your feet and your staff in your hand. And you shall eat it in haste. It is the Lord's passover.

"For the Lord will pass through to strike the Egyptians, and when he sees the blood upon the doortop and on the two side posts, the Lord will pass over the door, and will not allow death to come into your houses to strike you.

"And you shall observe this thing as a covenant with God for you and for your sons forever. It shall come to pass, when you come to the land which the Lord will give to you, according to his promise, that you shall keep this service. And when your children

say, 'What do you mean by this service?' you shall say, 'It is the sacrifice of the Lord's passover, for he passed over the houses of the children of Israel in Egypt when he struck down the Egyptians, and he saved all our families.'"

The people bowed their heads and worshiped. Then the children of Israel went away and did as the Lord had commanded Moses and Aaron.

And it came to pass at midnight that the Lord struck down all the first-born in the land of Egypt, from the first-born child of Pharaoh on his throne to the first-born of the captive in the dungeon, and all the first-born of cattle.

Pharaoh rose up in the night, he and all his servants, and all the Egyptians. And there was a great cry in Egypt, for there was not a house where someone was not dead.

Pharaoh called for Moses and Aaron by night, and said:

"Rise up and get out from among my people, both you and all the children of Israel. And go worship the Lord as you have asked. And take your flocks and your herds, as you asked, and be gone."

And the Egyptians urged the people, and tried to send them out of the land in haste, for they said, "We are all dead men."

So the people took their dough before it was raised, and bound their kneading boards up in their clothes bundles on their shoulders. And the people of Israel departed and journeyed from Rameses to Succoth. There were about six hundred thousand of them on foot, not counting the children, and there also went with them many other people, and large flocks and herds of cattle.

The night they went out of Egypt, the children of Israel had been living in Egypt for four hundred and thirty years.

CROSSING THE RED SEA

 ONTINUING their journey from Succoth, the Israelites camped at Etham, at the edge of the wilderness. And the Lord went before them by day in a pillar of cloud to show them the way, and by night in a pillar of fire to give them light, so that they could travel by day and night. He did not take away from the people the pillar of cloud by day nor the pillar of fire by night.

It was told to the king of Egypt that the people had fled, and the hearts of Pharaoh and his servants were moved against the people, and they said:

"Why have we done this, and let Israel free from serving us?"

Then Pharaoh made ready his chariots and took his people with him. He took six hundred chosen chariots, of all the chariots of Egypt, and put captains over all of them.

The Lord hardened the heart of Pharaoh, king of Egypt, and Pharaoh pursued the children of Israel, for the children of Israel had gone out proudly.

The Egyptians came after them, all the horses and chariots of Pharaoh, his horsemen and his army, and overtook them camping beside the sea, near Pihahiroth, before Baalzephon.

When Pharaoh came near, the children of Israel looked up, and, seeing the Egyptians marching after them, they were very frightened. Then the children of Israel cried out to the Lord, and they said to Moses:

"Were there no graves in Egypt? Have you brought us away to die in the wilderness? Why have you treated us in this way, in bringing us out of Egypt? Did we not tell you in Egypt, 'Let us alone, so that we may serve the Egyptians?' For it would have been better for us to serve the Egyptians than to die in the wilderness."

"Do not be afraid," said Moses to the people. "Stand still and watch the power of the Lord to save you, as he will show you today, for the Egyptians whom you have seen today you shall never see again. The Lord will fight for you if you will be calm."

THE ISRAELITES PASS THROUGH SAFELY

And God said to Moses:

"Why do you cry to me? Tell the children of Israel to go forward. But you must lift up your rod and stretch out your hand over the sea, and divide it. And the children of Israel shall go on dry land through the middle of the sea.

"And you shall see that I will harden the hearts of the Egyptians, and they shall follow you. Then I will show my power over Pharaoh and over all his armies, his chariots and his horsemen. And the Egyptians shall know that I am the Lord, when I have shown my power."

Then the angel of God which went before the camp of Israel moved and went behind them. The pillar of cloud moved from in front of them and rose up behind them. It came between the camp of Israel and the camp of the Egyptians, but it gave light by night to Israel, so that the Egyptians did not come near Israel all that night.

Then Moses stretched out his hand over the sea, and the Lord caused the sea to go back by making a strong east wind blow all that night. It made the sea dry land, and the waters were divided.

The children of Israel walked into the middle of the sea upon the dry ground, and the waters were a wall on their right hand and on their left.

The Egyptians pursued them and went into the middle of the sea after them, all Pharaoh's horses, his chariots and his horsemen.

When morning came, the Lord looked down on the army of the Egyptians through the pillar of fire and the cloud, and troubled the forces of the Egyptians. He made the wheels fall off their chariots and made them drive heavily, so that the Egyptians said, "Let us flee from the children of Israel, for the Lord fights for them against the Egyptians."

THE EGYPTIANS ARE DROWNED

Then God said to Moses:

"Stretch out your hand over the sea, so that the waters may come together again and cover the Egyptians, their chariots and their horsemen."

Moses stretched out his hand over the sea, and the sea returned to its bed when the morning appeared. The Egyptians fled before it, but the Lord overthrew the Egyptians in the middle of the sea. The waters returned and covered the chariots and the horsemen, and all the forces of Pharaoh that had followed him into the sea. Not one of them survived.

But the children of Israel had walked on dry land in the middle of the sea, and the waters had formed a wall for them on their right hand and on their left. Thus the Lord saved Israel that day from the hands of the Egyptians, and the Israelites saw the Egyptians dead upon the sea shore.

When Israel saw the great work the Lord did against the Egyptians, the people stood in awe of the Lord, and believed in him and his servant Moses.

Then Moses and the children of Israel sang this song to the Lord:

"I will sing to the Lord,
for he has triumphed gloriously;
The horse and his rider he has thrown into
the sea.
The Lord is my strength and song, and he has
become my savior;
He is my God, and I will prepare him a
house;
He is my father's God, I will exalt him.
Who is like thee, O Lord of all the gods?
Who is like thee, glorious in holiness?
In thy mercy thou hast led forth the people
thou hast saved;
In thy strength thou hast guided them to thy
holy dwelling."

And Miriam the prophetess, the sister of Aaron, took a timbrel in her hand, and all the women went out after her with timbrels and danced. And Miriam replied to them in song:

"Sing everyone to the Lord,
for he has triumphed gloriously;
The horse and his rider he has thrown into
the sea."

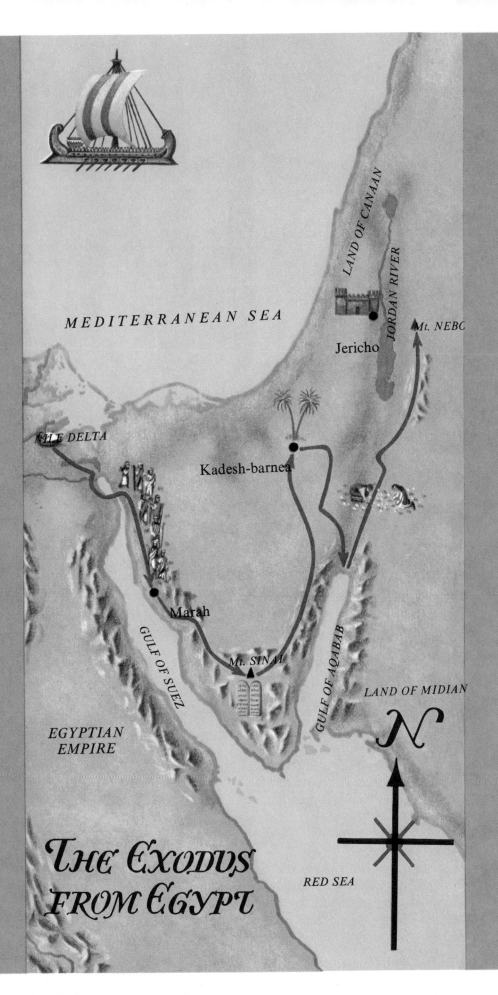

MEDITERRANEAN SEA

LAND OF CANAAN

JORDAN RIVER

Mt. NEBO

Jericho

NILE DELTA

Kadesh-barnea

Marah

GULF OF SUEZ

Mt. SINAI

GULF OF AQABAB

LAND OF MIDIAN

EGYPTIAN
EMPIRE

N

RED SEA

THE EXODUS
FROM EGYPT

THE
BITTER WELL
OF MARAH

O Moses led the Israelites from the Red Sea into the wilderness of Shur. They went for three days in the wilderness and found no water.

When at last they came to Marah, they could not drink the water there, for it was bitter. For this reason it was given the name of Marah, meaning "bitterness."

The people murmured against Moses, saying:

"What shall we drink?"

Moses cried to the Lord, and the Lord showed him a tree which, when he cast it into the waters, made the waters sweet. And there the Lord laid down a law for them, saying:

"If you will listen carefully to the voice of the Lord your God, and will do what is right in his sight, and will give ear to his commandments, and keep all his laws, I will not bring upon you any of those diseases which I brought upon the Egyptians, for I am the Lord who heals you."

Then they came to Elim, where there were twelve wells of water and seventy palm trees, and they camped beside the waters.

MANNA FROM HEAVEN

 NWARD from Elim they journeyed, and all the children of Israel came to the wilderness of Sin, which is between Elim and Sinai, on the fifteenth day of the second month after their departure from Egypt. And the children of Israel murmured against Moses and Aaron in the wilderness, saying:

"It would have been better for us to die by the hand of the Lord in the land of Egypt, when we sat down to bowls of meat and ate our fill of bread. For you have brought us out into this wilderness to kill all of us with hunger."

THE BREAD IS GATHERED

Then God said to Moses:

"You shall see. I will rain bread down from heaven for you. The people shall go out and gather a certain amount every day, so that I may test them, to see whether they will obey my laws or not. And it shall be arranged that on the sixth day they shall prepare what they bring in, which shall be twice as much as they gather on other days."

169

Moses and Aaron said to all the children of Israel:

"When evening comes, you shall know that it is the Lord who brought you out of the land of Egypt. And when morning comes, you shall see the glory of the Lord. For he has heard your murmurings against him. Your murmurings are not against us—for what are we?—but against the Lord."

And while Aaron was speaking to the congregation of the children of Israel, they looked out over the wilderness, and there they saw the glory of the Lord appear in a cloud.

Then God spoke to Moses, saying:

had disappeared, they saw lying on the face of the wilderness small round things, as small as hoarfrost, on the ground. And Moses said to them:

"This is the bread which the Lord has given to you to eat. And this is the commandment of the Lord: You are to gather an omer (about a tenth of a bushel) for each man, depending on how many you have to feed. Each man is to gather for those in his tents."

So the children of Israel went out and gathered the bread. Some took more and some took less, but when they measured it with an omer, those who had gathered a great deal had

"I have heard the murmuring of the children of Israel. Speak to them and say, 'In the evening you shall eat meat, and in the morning you shall have your fill of bread, and so you shall know that I am the Lord your God.'"

And it came to pass that in the evening quails flew up all over the camp, and in the morning dew lay all around the people. And when the dew

nothing over, and those who had gathered little had enough. Each man had enough to feed his people.

"Do not leave any of it until the morning," Moses said.

Nevertheless they did not listen to Moses, and some of them left it until the next morning, and it bred worms and smelled foul. And Moses was angry with them.

So they gathered the bread every morning, each man according to those he had to feed, and when the sun grew hot, it melted.

When the sixth day came, they gathered twice as much bread, two omers for each man. And all the rulers of the congregation came to Moses for directions. And he said to them:

"This is what the Lord has said: 'Tomorrow is the day of rest, the Lord's sabbath. Bake what you want to bake today, and boil what you want to boil, and what is left you may save, to keep for tomorrow.' "

So they laid it away until the next gather, and they found none. And the Lord said to Moses:

"How long will you refuse to keep my commandments and my laws? Because I have given you the sabbath, I give you the bread for two days on the sixth day. Let no man go out to seek food on the seventh day."

Now the house of Israel called the name of the food manna. It was white like coriander seeds, and the taste of it was like wafers made with honey.

And Moses spoke to the people, saying: "The Lord has commanded that an omer of manna shall be kept

morning, as Moses told them, and it did not smell bad, nor was there a single worm in it. And Moses said:

"Eat today, for today is the Lord's sabbath. Today you shall not find bread in the field. Six days you are to gather it, but on the seventh day, which is the sabbath, there shall be none." And so it was, for some of the people went out on the seventh day to

for your descendants, so that they may see the bread which was given to you in the wilderness, when you were brought from the land of Egypt."

And he commanded Aaron to take a pot and to put an omer of manna into it, to be kept for this purpose.

And the children of Israel ate manna forty years, until they came to the borders of the land of Canaan.

WATER FROM THE ROCK

UT it came to pass that when the children of Israel had left the wilderness of Sin, and had pitched their camp in Rephidim, they found that there was no water for them to drink.

Therefore they complained to Moses and said:

"Give us water that we may drink. Why did you bring us out of Egypt, to kill us and our children and our cattle with thirst?"

Moses cried to the Lord, saying:

"What shall I do to these people? They are almost ready to stone me."

God said:

"Go on before the people, and take with you the elders of Israel. Take in your hand the rod which you used to strike the river, and go. I will stand before you there upon the rock in Horeb. And you shall strike the rock, and water shall come out of it so that the people may drink."

And this Moses did, while the elders of Israel looked on.

Moses gave to this place the name of Massah, meaning "temptation," because the children of Israel tempted the Lord and tried to test him, saying, "Is the Lord with us, or not?"

THE DEFEAT OF AMALEK

MALEK came with his army and attacked the people of Israel as they camped in Rephidim. And Moses said to Joshua:

"Choose men and go out and fight with Amalek. Tomorrow I will stand on the top of the hill with the rod of God in my hand."

So Joshua did as Moses had said to him, and fought with Amalek. And Moses, Aaron and Hur went up to the top of the hill. And it came to pass that when Moses held up his hand, Israel was victorious, and when he let down his hand, Amalek was victorious.

But Moses' hands became weary, so they took a stone and put it under him, and he sat on it. And Aaron and Hur held up his hands, the one on the one side and the other on the other.

Thus Moses' hands were steady until the going down of the sun. And Joshua defeated Amalek and his people.

JETHRO ADVISES MOSES

WHEN Jethro, the priest of Midian, Moses' father-in-law, heard of all that God had done for Moses and for Israel his people, he came to see Moses in the wilderness.

Moses went out to meet his father-in-law and told him all that the Lord had done to Pharaoh and to the Egyptians for Israel's sake. And Jethro said:

"Blessed be the Lord. Now I know that he is greater than all gods."

And it came to pass on the next day that Moses sat to judge the people, and the people stood by Moses from the morning to the evening. And when Jethro saw this, he said:

"What is this thing that you do with the people? Why do you sit by yourself alone, and why do all the people stand by you from morning to evening?"

And Moses said to his father-in-law: "The people come to me to inquire of God. When they have a matter, they come to me, and I make them know the statutes of God, and his laws."

And Moses' father-in-law said to him: "The thing that you do is not good. You will surely wear away, both you and this people who are with you. For this thing is too heavy for you. You are not able to perform it by yourself alone. Listen now to my voice, I will give you advice.

"You should choose from the people able men, men who fear God, men of truth and honesty. Place them over the people, to be rulers of thousands, and rulers of hundreds, rulers of fifties and rulers of tens. And let them judge the people at all times. Every great matter they shall bring to you, but every small matter they shall judge themselves. Thus shall it be easier for you, and they shall share the

burden with you. If you shall do this thing, and God so commands you, then you shall be able to endure, and all this people also shall go to their place in peace."

Moses listened to the voice of his father-in-law, and did all that he said. He chose able men from all Israel and made them rulers of thousands, rulers of hundreds, rulers of fifties, and rulers of tens. And they judged the people at all times. The difficult cases they brought to Moses, but every small matter they judged themselves.

And Moses let his father-in-law depart. And he went his way into his own land.

from the
BOOK OF PSALMS

PSALMS OF CELEBRATION AND PRAISE

Psalm 66

Make a joyful noise unto God, all ye lands.
Sing forth the honour of his name;
  make his praise glorious.
Say unto God, How terrible art thou
  in thy works!
  through the greatness of thy power
  shall thine enemies
  submit themselves unto thee.
All the earth shall worship thee,
  and shall sing unto thee;
  they shall sing to thy name.

Come and see the works of God:
  he is terrible in his doing toward
  the children of men.
He turned the sea into dry land:
  they went through the flood on foot:
  there did we rejoice in him.
He ruleth by his power for ever;
  his eyes behold the nations:
  let not the rebellious exalt themselves.

O bless our God, ye people,
  and make the voice of his praise to be heard;
Which holdeth our soul in life,
  and suffereth not our feet to be moved.
For thou, O God, hast proved us:
  thou hast tried us, as silver is tried.
Thou broughtest us into the net;
  thou laidst affliction upon our loins.
Thou hast caused men to ride over our heads:
  we went through fire and through water;
  but thou broughtest us out into a wealthy plac

Psalm 98

O sing unto the Lord a new song;
   for he hath done marvellous things:
   his right hand, and his holy arm,
   hath gotten him the victory.
The Lord hath made known his salvation:
   his righteousness hath he openly shewed
   in the sight of the heathen.
He hath remembered his mercy and his truth
   toward the house of Israel:
   all the ends of the earth have seen
   the salvation of our God.

Make a joyful noise unto the Lord, all the earth;
   make a loud noise, and rejoice, and sing praise.
Sing unto the Lord with the harp;
   with the harp, and the voice of a psalm.
With trumpets and sound of cornet,
   make a joyful noise before the Lord, the King.

Let the sea roar, and the fulness thereof;
   the world, and they that dwell therein.
Let the floods clap their hands:
   let the hills be joyful together
Before the Lord: for he cometh to judge
   the earth; with righteousness shall he judge
   the world, and the people with equity.

Psalm 150

Praise ye the Lord.
   Praise God in his sanctuary:
   praise him in the firmament of his power.
Praise him for his mighty acts:
   praise him according to
   his excellent greatness.

Praise him with the sound of the trumpet:
   praise him with the psaltery and harp.
Praise him with the timbrel and dance:
   praise him with stringed instruments
   and organs.
Praise him upon the loud cymbals:
   praise him upon the high sounding cymbals.
Let every thing that hath breath praise the Lord.
   Praise ye the Lord.

Psalm 105

O give thanks unto the Lord:
call upon his name;
make known his deeds among the people.
Sing unto him, sing psalms unto him:
talk ye of all his wondrous works.
Glory ye in his holy name:
let the heart of them rejoice
that seek the Lord.
Seek the Lord, and his strength;
seek his face evermore.
Remember his marvellous works
that he hath done; his wonders,
and the judgments of his mouth;
O ye seed of Abraham his servant,
ye children of Jacob his chosen.

He is the Lord our God;
his judgments are in all the earth.
He hath remembered his covenant for ever,
the word which he commanded
to a thousand generations:
Which covenant he made with Abraham,
and his oath unto Isaac;
And confirmed the same unto Jacob for a law,
and to Israel for an everlasting covenant;
Saying, Unto thee will I give the land
of Canaan, the lot of your inheritance:

When they were but a few men in number;
yea, very few, and strangers in it.
When they went from one nation to another,
from one kingdom to another people,
He suffered no man to do them wrong:
yea, he reproved kings for their sakes;
Saying, Touch not mine anointed,
and do my prophets no harm.

Moreover, he called for a famine upon the land
he brake the whole staff of bread.
He sent a man before them,
even Joseph, who was sold for a servant;
Whose feet they hurt with fetters:
he was laid in iron;
Until the time that his word came;
the word of the Lord tried him.
The king sent and loosed him;
even the ruler of the people
and let him go free.
He made him lord of his house,
and ruler of all his substance;
To bind his princes at his pleasure,
and teach his senators wisdom.

Israel also came into Egypt,
and Jacob sojourned in the land of Ham.
And he increased his people greatly,
and made them stronger than their enemies.
He turned their heart to hate his people,
to deal subtilly with his servants.

He sent Moses his servant,
and Aaron whom he had chosen.
They shewed his signs among them,
and wonders in the land of Ham.
He sent darkness, and made it dark;
and they rebelled not against his word.
He turned their waters into blood,
and slew their fish.
Their land brought forth frogs in abundance,
in the chambers of their kings.
He spake, and there came divers sorts of flies,
and lice in all their coasts.
He gave them hail for rain,
and flaming fire in their land.
He smote their vines also, and their fig trees;
and brake the trees of their coasts.
He spake, and the locusts came, and caterpillars,
and that without number,
And did eat up all the herbs in their land,
and devoured the fruit of their ground.
He smote also all the firstborn in their land,
the chief of all their strength.

He brought them forth also with silver and gold;
and there was not one feeble person
among their tribes.
Egypt was glad when they departed;
for the fear of them fell upon them.
He spread a cloud for a covering,
and fire to give light in the night.
The people asked, and he brought quails,
and satisfied them with the bread of heaven.
He opened the rock, and the waters gushed out;
they ran in the dry places like a river.
For he remembered his holy promise,
and Abraham his servant.

And he brought forth his people with joy,
and his chosen with gladness;
And gave them the lands of the heathen:
and they inherited the labour of the people;
That they might observe his statutes,
and keep his laws.
Praise ye the Lord.

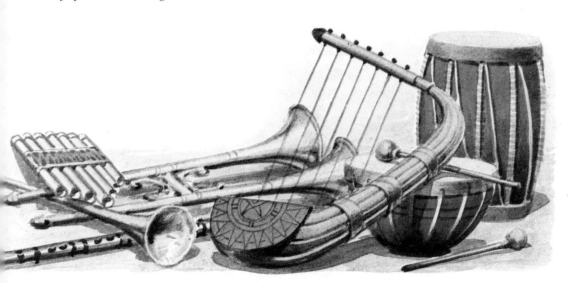

ILLUSTRATED
GLOSSARY

Aaron the Levite (p. 148)

Aaron was Moses' older brother and became the first high priest of the Israelites.

Abominations (p. 156)

Something hateful is called an abomination. When Moses said that the Hebrew religion was "an abomination to the Egyptians," he meant that they could not understand the Hebrew belief in one God. Not understanding the belief, they were afraid of it and disliked it.

When the Hebrews spoke of abominations they usually meant the worship of idols and false gods.

Amalekites (p. 174)

The Amalekites were a tribe that lived in the desert south of the Holy Land. They were enemies of the Hebrews.

Bitter herbs (p. 162)

Moses instructed his people to eat bitter herbs, probably lettuce, endive, chicory, or other sharp-tasting greens. Today, bitter herbs are part of the traditional Passover meal.

Bulrushes (p. 142)

Bulrushes are reeds that grow in marshy or wet places. One kind of bulrush that grows in the Nile is papyrus. The ancient Egyptians used its leaves as a fragile writing paper.

Children of Israel (p. 147)

The children of Israel are the descendents of Jacob, whom God renamed Israel. From Jacob's twelve sons came the Twelve Tribes of Israel, who are also called the Hebrews, or the Israelites.

Coriander (p. 171)

Coriander is an herb somewhat like parsley. It grew wild all over the Holy Land, and its seeds and leaves were used to season food. Coriander was a sacred plant to the Egyptians and its seeds were found in Egyptian tombs.

Elim (p. 169)

Elim was an oasis in the western part of the Sinai Peninsula.

Etham (p. 164)

Etham was located on the western shore of the Sea of Reeds, north of the Red Sea.

Herb (p. 162)

Herbs are plants used to season food. The herb Moses told the Israelites to dip in lamb's blood was hyssop, a plant that we now call marjoram. This herb is used to flavor meat and other dishes.

Hoarfrost (p. 170)

A thin white covering of frost is called hoarfrost. It forms when the temperature falls below freezing and the dew on the ground turns to frost.

Horeb (p. 146)

Horeb was another name for Mount Sinai. This mountain is in the southern part of the Sinai Peninsula.

Horses (p. 157)

The Hyksos, a Semitic people who invaded Egypt before the time of Joseph, brought small horses with them from their homeland in Asia. When the Hebrews were in Egypt, they saw these animals for the first time. When the Hebrews returned to Canaan they preferred to use asses or donkeys, because the small donkey was a better animal for the dry and hilly land of their new home. Much later the Hebrew kings used large numbers of horses in warfare.

Joshua (p. 174)

Joshua was a young man chosen by Moses to be his assistant after the Israelites left Egypt.

Joshua, the son of Nun, was originally named Hoshea, but Moses changed his name to Joshua. Such a name change was not unusual among the Israelites. Abraham's name had been Abram, and Israel had been known as Jacob.

Joshua is known as a great soldier who was victorious in many battles. But Moses trusted him for many other tasks. In later years, Joshua was the only person permitted to stay with Moses when the Lord spoke to him. As time went on, Joshua's responsibilities became greater and greater.

The king who did not know Joseph (p. 140)

The pharaoh who came to the throne of Egypt three hundred years after Joseph's death was apparently part of a new royal family who had no knowledge of Joseph's deeds. By this time the Hebrews had been in the land of Goshen for more than four hundred years.

A land of milk and honey (p. 147)

In the Bible, a place where there is always plenty to eat and drink is called a land of milk and honey. In their wanderings in the desert, the Israelites were often hungry and thirsty, so they thought of a good land as one where there would always be enough to eat and drink. Most of all, it would be a land where their favorite foods, milk and honey, were plentiful.

Levi, The family of (p. 142)

The people descended from Jacob's third son, Levi, were called Levites. The Levites were the religious leaders of the Israelites. They served as priests, or priests' helpers, offering sacrifices to God. Moses and Aaron belonged to the tribe of Levi.

Locusts (p. 159)

A locust is a kind of grasshopper. When the weather and the food supply are just right for them, locusts can become terrible pests. They become so numerous they can cover the countryside like a black cloud, shutting out the sun. Large numbers of locusts will eat every plant in sight, and leave behind fields stripped of every growing thing.

"Made the water sweet" (p. 168)

When the Israelites first tasted the water at Marah, it was too salty to drink. After Moses made it sweet, it was pleasant and refreshing. "Sweet" here does not mean sugary, but fit to drink.

Midian (p. 144)

Midian was located in the northwestern part of the Arabian Peninsula. The people of Midian, the Midianites, were Semites like the Hebrews. Because they were both Semites, the Hebrews and the Midianites were friends. Moses married a Midianite woman, whose name was Zipporah.

Miriam (p. 166)

Miriam was the sister of Aaron and Moses. It was probably Miriam who watched over the baby Moses when he was hidden in the bulrushes.

Pahahiroth and Baalzephon (p. 164)

No one knows exactly where these places were. However, we do know they were in northeastern Egypt, near where the Israelites crossed the Red Sea.

The Passover (p. 162)

God punished the pharaoh and the Egyptians by striking down the first-born child of each family, but he spared the Hebrews' families. This night of death when the Lord passed over the children of Israel and instructed them to prepare to flee Egypt is called the Lord's Passover.

The Jewish people still celebrate that night with a feast called a Seder. It is traditional to serve many of the same foods that were served at that first Passover. On the Seder table are a roasted lamb bone, bitter herbs (see Bitter herbs), boiled eggs, salt water, fruit, nuts, and wine. And during the holy time of Passover, only unleavened bread (see Unleavened bread) is served, just like the bread the Israelites were instructed to make in haste.

Pithom and Rameses (p. 140)

Pithom and Rameses were both treasure cities (see Treasure cities) built on the delta of the Nile River in Goshen, the Egyptian home of the Hebrews. A brick wall was built around Pithom, and in the city itself many brick storerooms were erected.

Promise to Abraham, to Isaac, and to Jacob (p. 146)

God had made a covenant with the patriarchs to give their people the land of Canaan.

Quails (p. 170)

Quails are small brown birds that eat seeds and insects. The quails of the Bible are not as big as the quails we see today in North America. The Israelites thought quails were very good to eat.

Rameses to Succoth (p. 163)

These two places were in northern Egypt. Rameses was built on the delta of the Nile River. Succoth was near the present Suez Canal.

Rephidim (p. 142)

Rephidim was a town in the southern part of the Sinai Peninsula. Here the Hebrews turned east. Here, too, Moses again met some of his father-in-law's people, the friendly Midianites.

Sabbath (p. 171)

The Sabbath day is the day of rest and the day of worship. The seventh day of the week, the day we call Saturday, was the Hebrews' Sabbath. The Sabbath, meaning "to rest," was the only day of the week for which the Hebrews had a name. To them it was a day of great holiness. It was celebrated because God had rested on that day from the work of making the world.

On the Hebrews' Sabbath no work of any kind was to be done. Not even the farm animals were allowed to work.

The Sabbath began at sunset on Friday evening and continued until sunset the next day. But the Sabbath was much more to the Hebrews than a day of rest. It was a day to honor God.

Much later in Jewish history, it once happened that some Hebrews were attacked by soldiers on the Sabbath. They refused to take up swords to defend themselves on that holy day, and they were all killed.

Straw to make bricks (p. 150)

The Egyptians and Israelites used mud mixed with chopped straw to make bricks. Workers sometimes did the mixing with their feet. The material was then shaped in wooden molds, and the molded bricks were set out in the sun to dry. Bricks for use in foundations and the lower parts of walls were sometimes baked in kilns, or ovens, to make them especially strong.

"They are almost ready to stone me" (p. 173)

In biblical times, criminals were often put to death by stoning. They were

The wilderness of Sinai, through which Moses led the Hebrews.

taken outside the camp, and large stones were cast at them until they died.

Timbrel (p. 166)

A timbrel was an instrument like a small drum or tambourine. Some timbrels were small and flat with skins stretched over both sides. Others were round or square and had skins stretched over only one side. Timbrels of both kinds were used to beat a rhythm.

Treasure cities (p. 140)

Cities where supplies were stored for the pharaoh's troops were called treasure cities. The pharaoh greatly feared that enemies would attack his country from the northeast. If that were to happen, his troops who were fighting in the delta would need a nearby source of supplies. The pharaoh used the Hebrews as slave labor to build the treasure cities of Pithom and Rameses. (See Pithom and Rameses.)

Unleavened bread (p. 162)

Bread that has not been raised by yeast or baking soda is called unleavened bread. To make bread light and airy, the people of biblical times counted on natural yeast from the air. They left dough standing for several days, or added a bit of the leavened dough kept from the bread made the day before. Women of those days baked their small, flat, round breads every day except the Sabbath, when no work, including cooking, was done.

During the first Passover, the Hebrews didn't have time for their bread to rise. They had to bake it in haste and so ate unleavened bread. (See The Passover.)

"Who is the Lord?" (p. 150)

The pharaoh asked Moses who his Lord was, because the Egyptians did not share the Hebrews' belief in one God. The people of Egypt believed in a number of gods.

Wilderness of Shur (p. 168)

The area that stretched across the northern part of the Sinai Peninsula was called the wilderness of Shur. In the Bible, the word "wilderness" is used for a wild, deserted place where no crops were raised and few, if any, people lived.